This igloo book belongs to:

_____

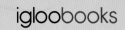

Published in 2016
by Igloo Books Ltd
Cottage Farm
Sywell
NN6 0BJ
www.igloobooks.com

Original story by Igloo Books Ltd
Party Paws™ & A Little Bear Called Bamboo™
are registered Trade Marks of © Artworld Inspirations Limited

REX001 0816
4 6 8 10 9 7 5 3
ISBN: 978-1-78440-497-0
Printed and manufactured in China

Mommy and Me

igloobooks

I love my mommy because we
have so much fun together every day.

My mommy is snuggly and soft
and she always cuddles me tight.

I love to paint pictures for Mommy. She hangs them on the wall and says how pretty they are.

When Mommy is going out, I help
her to find her best shoes and purse.

I love to go in the backyard with Mommy.
It's fun to chase the butterflies as they flutter past.

I grow pretty flowers in
my own special flower bed.

I give Mommy some of my
flowers because I love her so much.

When I fall over, Mommy hugs
me tight and kisses me better.

When it's Mommy's birthday, I make
her a special birthday cup of hot chocolate.

I give her lots of presents. I wrap them in pretty paper and tie them up with ribbons.

When it's my birthday I
get presents and balloons, too.

Mommy bakes me an extra yummy
birthday cake with a cherry on top.

Mommy makes me lots of tasty
things to eat. I like sandwiches the best.

Sometimes, if I'm really lucky,
Mommy lets me have a special treat.

I love to play with my toys,
but Mommy says I always make a mess.

At the end of the day, Mommy helps me put
my toys away, but I always keep my special bunny.

Mommy runs me a bubbly bath before bedtime and makes sure that I'm clean.

Every night, Mommy reads me a bedtime story before I go to sleep.

Before I go to bed and snuggle in,
I say good night to Mommy and Daddy.

Mommy tucks me tightly into bed and
gives me a lovely good night kiss.

My mommy is the best in the whole world and that's why I love her.